Y0-ART-757

FITNESS FUN WITH
SPORT GOOFY

© THE WALT DISNEY COMPANY

Sponsored by:

Minute Maid.
IN-THE-BOX
and your retailer

"Minute Maid" is a registered trademark of The Coca-Cola Company.

It was Goofy's first day as the new gym coach at Feel Fit Elementary School, and he was ready for fun! For weeks, he had been planning activities and games to teach the children during gym and recess. In fact, he had an especially exciting surprise for them!

Goofy blew his whistle and the kids came running! "Hi gang!," Goofy greeted them. "We're going to have a great year ahead of us at Feel Fit Elementary. But the best news is that our school has been invited to compete in a track meet against Good Health Elementary across town in a few weeks!"

"Hurray!" Everyone cheered. "What are we waiting for? Let's start practicing now!" A boy yelled. He started to race in circles.

"Whoa there!" Goofy said. "First we need to stretch and warm up so our muscles don't get strained or hurt." Goofy showed everyone some stretching exercises they could do anytime.

Try these exercises yourself!

Feet apart, hands on waist. Lean from side to side.

Arms straight out. Small circles forward, then backward.

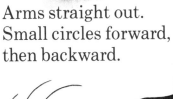

Feet apart, arms out. Touch right toe with left hand. Come up. Touch left toe with right hand.

Get in a runner's starting position with one leg back. Bounce gently. Change legs and repeat.

"Now that we're warmed up, we can do some exercises to help your heart and lungs grow strong," Goofy told the children. "First let's run in place!"

Just then, Goofy saw two children, Jason and Sarah, just sitting by themselves, watching. "What's wrong?" Goofy hurried over to ask them.

"Come on and join us! Physical education gives you a good break from sitting at your desks." Goofy told Jason and Sarah. But they shook their heads.

"We're too tired, Goofy," Sarah said sadly. "Can we just watch today?"

Goofy went back to the other children, but he was trying to think of some way to get Sarah and Jason to join the fun.

Goofy showed the children some more exercises. "These are aerobic exercises," he explained. "They're good for your heart and lungs. Don't try to go too fast. If you get tired, slow down, but just keep moving."

Jump in place and swing your arms from side to side.

Run in place and make swimming motions with your arms.

Put your left hand in air. Bounce to the left. Put your right hand up and bounce to the right.

Now, you try too! Remember to start off slowly and work up gradually.

Suddenly Goofy had an idea! "Come on Jason and Sarah," he called. "We're going for a nature walk around the neighborhood. Let's see how many different animals and plants you can find for science class."

Jason and Sarah perked up. They both liked animals. As Goofy's class walked along, they saw two grey squirrels, a kitten, a baby bird and five different kinds of trees.

"That was fun!" Jason said when they returned to the schoolyard. "Yup!" Goofy laughed. "Walking is great aerobic exercise. So are swimming, bicycling and jumping rope!"

The lunch bell rang. Jason pulled a bag of chips from his backpack. Sarah munched a chocolate donut. "Want some?" they asked Goofy. "Gawrsh, no thanks," Goofy said. "Those are fun treats sometimes, but you should eat more nutritious food everyday to feel your very best." Then Goofy had another good idea.

The very next day, Goofy came to school with a huge picnic basket and lots of grocery bags.

"What's inside?" All the children asked, but Goofy just grinned. "Go into your classes now, and you'll see at lunchtime," he promised.

Inside the basket and bags were lots of good things to eat. When no one was looking, Goofy hid the food all over the playground, under the jungle gym, next to the basketball court and even around the softball field.

When the lunch bell rang, he sent the children on a treasure hunt to find the delicious surprises for their lunch. Some of the other teachers even joined the fun. Soon, everyone was enjoying a lunch complete with lots of cool, refreshing fruit juice to drink.

"My apple is crisp and sweet," Jason remarked. "I was thirsty," Sarah said. "This fruit juice is just right!"

Here's what Goofy hid for lunch:

Yogurt

Cool, creamy yogurt (also milk, cheese and ice cream) gives calcium and vitamin D for teeth and bones.

Apples, Bananas and Strawberries

Sweet Fruit and Juice (and vegetables too) give vitamins C, A, iron and calcium for your skin, eyes, bones and blood.

Peanut Butter Sandwiches on Whole Wheat Bread

Nuts, beans, meat or eggs give protein for muscles. Whole grains supply iron and vitamin B for your blood, skin and nervous system.

Feel hungry? Have a healthy snack with any of these foods!

Sarah was very late the next day. She came to school walking very slowly, yawning and rubbing her eyes. "I stayed up late last night to watch a movie on TV," she yawned. "It was good, but boy am I tired today! I got up so late I didn't have time for breakfast!"

"That's what happens when you don't get enough sleep," Goofy told the children. But Sarah didn't hear him! She had fallen asleep!

"I need to do something fast!" Goofy thought. He jumped up and began waving his arms in the air. "Hey everybody, do what I do!" he yelled as he began to cheer:

"A good breakfast and a full night's rest make every day your very best!"

Soon the children were jumping and cheering right along with Goofy till the school playground rang with laughter.

Make up your own motions to Goofy's goofy cheer!

The day of the track meet was drawing near. Every day the Feel Fit Elementary students stretched and warmed up, ran, skipped and hopped, ate good lunches and got plenty of rest. Even Jason and Sarah were joining in. Jason was practicing for the softball toss.

"I'm not tired, anymore," he told Goofy. "But I wish my arms were stronger so I could throw farther."

"Try these exercises," Goofy replied. "Start with a few and slowly work up to doing more."

Lie on your stomach. Put your feet together and your arms in front of you. Push up on your elbows and lift your chest from the floor. Lower slowly and repeat.

Place your palms against a wall at shoulder height. Bend your elbows and touch the wall with your chin. Push away from the wall with your arms. Keep your body straight.

Hold your arms straight out in front of you. Make fists. Ask a friend to grasp your wrists. Try to raise your arms while your friend pushes down. Count to five. Relax.

Go ahead and give these a try too, to make your arms, shoulders and back grow stronger.

Sarah was feeling better every day too! She wanted to be on the girls' relay team, and try the long jump. "But Goofy, I can't jump very far. What can I do to make my legs stronger?" she asked.

Goofy showed Sarah some of his favorite ways to strengthen the muscles in his legs.

Sit on a chair. Raise both legs and do a flutter-kick with legs straight.

Squat on your toes with your hands behind your back. Push up from your toes and leap as high as you can.

Lie on your back and lift each leg straight up. Now try with both legs at once.

You try too. Start by repeating each exercise twice and work up to as many as you can do.

At last, the day of the big meet arrived. Jason and Sarah were excited, and so were all the other students! "I'm so nervous I can hardly stand it!" Sarah frowned. "I know trying my best is the most important thing, but right now I'm too tense to do anything!"

"Gawrsh, Sarah," Goofy said. "A few deep breaths always help calm me down whenever I am tense or tired. Try some with me!"

Sit with your back straight and relaxed. Put your hands on your tummy just above your belly button. Close your eyes and breathe in slowly through your nose. Push your tummy out against your hands, then slowly expand your chest. Hold and count to three. Breathe slowly out through your nose. Repeat three times.

Take a few deep breaths right now! Feel relaxed and calm? You should!

With a blast of the whistle, the meet began! In the bleachers, all the teachers, friends and families of the students from Feel Fit Elementary and Good Health Elementary cheered and shouted.

Goofy watched his students. They were trying hard, and he was very proud of them. "That's the way!" he called. "Do your best and have fun!"

It was a wonderful track meet and a wonderful day! Jason won a trophy for throwing a softball the farthest. Sarah's relay team came in second. Her long jump wasn't the longest, but it was the best she'd ever done before, and she was proud of herself. The Good Health students did well too, so everyone was happy!

"Hurray for Goofy," Jason and Sarah yelled. "He's a champ." "No, you are!" Goofy laughed. "You're the fitness champions of Feel Fit School." "Well hurray for us, then," everyone began to cheer.

We eat right and get our sleep
And we're always moving to the beat!
We're fitness champs—so we should know.
Staying fit is the way to go!